W0008324

"Maybe you are searching
Amongst the branches,
For what only appears in the
Roots."

- RUMI

Copyright © 2021 by Jade Cummings.
All rights reserved.
Printed in the United States of America.
No part of this book may be used
or reproduced in any manner whatsoever without written permission
except in the case of reprints in the context of reviews.

JADE MAGIC Publishing
Hawthorne Healing Center
21 Hawthorne St., Medford, Oregon 97504
www.hawthornehealingcenter.com
www.jade-magic.com

Library of Congress Control Number: 2022902687

ISBN: 978-0-578-35863-5

JADE MAGIC
PUBLISHING

FIRST EDITION

Illustrations & Cover Design: Jade Cummings
Editor: Jeremiah Zuba

To Carley & my Mother.

———

May you find The Light
in the darkness
of our Roots.

" There is nothing more real
or more practical in this
UNIVERSE than MYSTICISM —
remember that...And it's usually
sitting right smack in the middle
of GRIEF. "

- BRANDI CARLILE
Broken Horses: A Memoir

THE SEED
A POETIC JOURNEY

By
Jade Cummings

JADE MAGIC
PUBLISHING

I SEE A SEED

Full of brilliance
Power
Need;

A need to be
Seen
To be planted
With room to
Grow,

But first
Buried
In the dark
Where it takes
Time to sow.

Once the SEED
Awakens from its
Dark Night of the
Soul

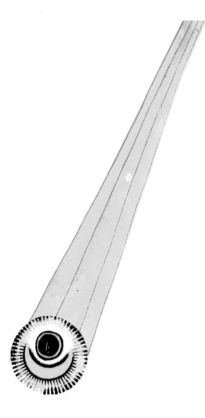

It finds its way by
Feeling.

A crack,
A glimmer,
A glow
Shines in
From that
Dark hole.

The SEED opens her eyes;
A gentle caress of her cheek.
She is welcomed into this new world
By a sound that is unique.

A melody within
A whisper.
She is carried softly into the air.
A rising
Into flight
With the utmost care.

"Who's there?"
Asked the SEED.

"I am the AIR you breathe,"
Whispered the WIND.

"Where am I going?"
Asked the SEED.

"This way,"
Whispered the WIND.

"But what will I become?"
Asked the SEED.

"A new way,"
Whispered the WIND.

"But how will I know I am there?"
Asked the SEED.

"When you no longer
Choose to stay."

Guidance
Is offered.
Nourishment
From the SUN
And the RAIN.

Now the
Growth
Process has started,
The SEED's
Life energy expands
Through its veins.

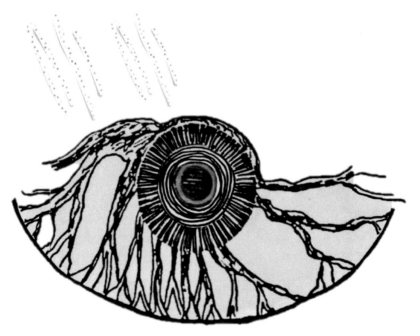

The SEED
Let out a sigh,
Took a deep breath,
And let go.

Then she noticed
A tiny leaf
Sprouting
Down below.

"I'm growing!"
Shouted the SPROUT.

"Yes you are,"
Whispered the EARTH.

"Part of growth
Means surrender
To the timing,"
Whispered the EARTH.

So the SPROUT
Took a deep
Breath...

And then another...

Soaking up the soil
Enjoying the warmth
Of her Mother.

But then the clouds
Rolled in
Blocking the SUN
And bringing
RAIN.
The SPROUT
Felt the discomfort
Of grief
And all its pain.

"This hurts!"
Yelled the SPROUT.

"It will pass,"
Whispered the WATER.

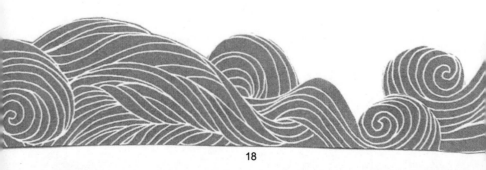

"But I am lonely,"
Said the SPROUT.

"Yes, but you're not alone,"
Whispered the WATER.

"Everyone is lonely,
But you must still reach out.
We are created for connection;
Not to live without."

"Part of relationship
Is having someone to
Hug and hold;
Someone to sit with
In silence and
Laughter
When you're old."

"I do love to laugh,"
Agreed the SPROUT.
"Maybe I will reach out."

So the SPROUT
Stretched out
Her roots
To find others
Different and alike.

Some she laughed with
Some she cried with
And some she realized
Had energy
She didn't like.

But before
The SPROUT
Could notice,
The RAIN -
It had thinned.

And with laughter,
The SPROUT
Twirled and danced
In the WIND.

More leaves
Had spouted
And she grew
Taller than before.

It was then
She noticed
At the center
Of herself,
A door.

It was FIRE
That came knocking.
A desire
Grew inside.

"What's this longing?"
Asked the NEW LEAF,
"And why do I want to hide?"

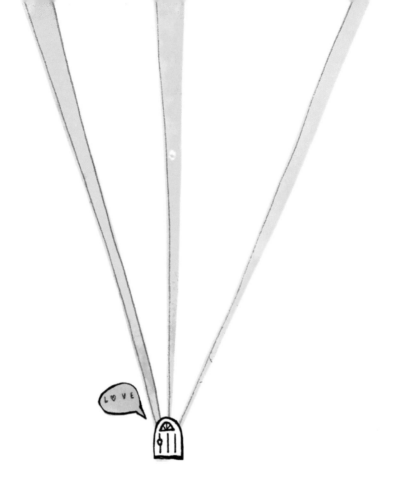

"It's called LOVE,"
Whispered FIRE.

"This is why you're here.

Now you get to choose
Who and *What*
You let near."

"But I want it all!"
Shouted the NEW LEAF.

"Careful,"
Whispered FIRE.

"Not everyone or
Everything is safe
Or supportive,"
Warned the FIRE.

But the NEW LEAF
Felt desire
Knocking on her door
Once more.

With eagerness
She opened herself
With an invitation
To explore.

Her trunk expanded
And her branches
Stretched wide,
Making space to offer
Herself to anyone
Who cried.

"Here, come sit in my shade.
Let me offer you rest
And a listening ear."

With delight
Many came,
Each sharing their
Secrets and a Tear.

Every teardrop
Contained their grief,
But also in it,
Their
Shame.

So each teardrop
She absorbed
Held a poison
She couldn't name.

As the TREE
Continued to open
Her Door
To those
Who would knock,

She began to notice
Different pains
In her body
She could not
Unlock.

"How do I fix myself?"
Asked the TREE.

"By learning to digest poison,"
Whispered the SUN.

"So I need to change what I eat?"
Asked the TREE.

The SUN
Caressed her leaves
With sweet affection.

"Sometimes,"
Whispered the SUN.

"Nourishment comes
In many forms.

What you allow yourself
To taste, touch, and feel -
Transforms."

"But I love so much!"
Said the TREE.

"Yes, I know,"
Whispered the SUN.

"That's why you're here -
To turn poison
Into healing,
My Sacred One."

So the TREE
Tried to offer more
By shedding her leaves
To absorb all the tears.

She extended her branches
To others
For many, many
Years.

Exhausted and depleted,
The TREE
Hadn't noticed
The brewing Storm.

The Sky grew dark,
And Thunder began to form.

Without warning,
A Lightening bolt hit!

She stood breathless
As every part of herself
Split.

Heart broken
By betrayal -
How was it possible
That LOVE could fail?

"I can't trust anyone!"
Mourned the STUMP.

"And how can I even trust myself?"

"I am so sorry,"
Whispered the MOON.

"LOVE and GRIEF
Are both SEEDS of The Self."

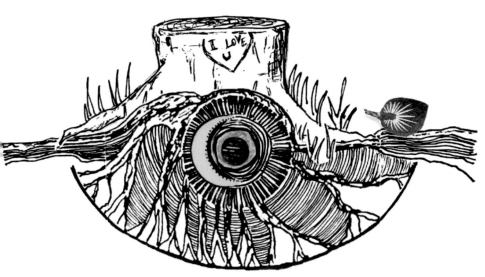

"But how do I put myself back together?"
Asked the STUMP.

"With time,"
Whispered the MOON.

"On the path to forgiveness,
Only each heart
Knows how soon."

And so the STUMP
Remained divided.
Should she
Stay
Or should she
Go?

"Not yet,"
Whispered the MOON,
"There is still so much
You need to know."

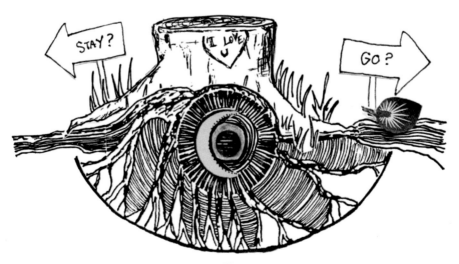

So she stayed
With nothing more to give.

No more leaves,
No more branches -
Only her ROOTS
Who whispered...

"LIVE."

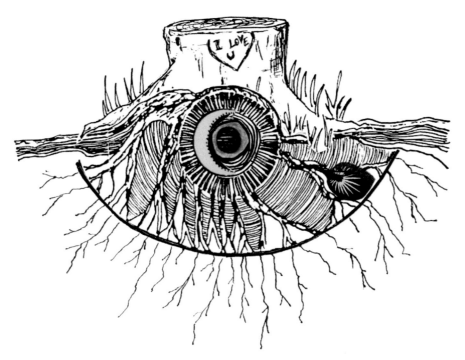

And so instead of
Growing up,
She shifted her energy
To ROOT down.

Returning to where
She came from,
The STUMP
Discovered something
Profound.

As she followed
The pathway of each
ROOT,
She saw a glimpse
Into the past.

Each story
Of every Tear
Was woven tightly
To the last.

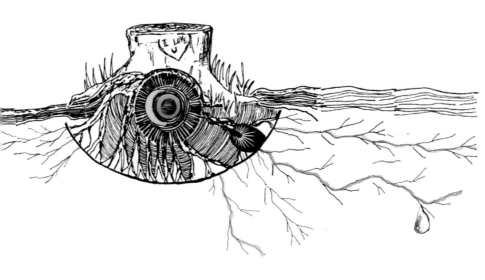

When she held up
Each Tear,
Shed from others
She had known,

Each Tear became a
MIRROR
Reflecting a story
Of her own.

She came face to face
With her
VICTIM
Who felt powerless and weak.

Always feeling
Taken advantage of;
Forced to fend for the meek.

She came face to face
With her
INNER CHILD
Who didn't get
What she longed for.

"Yes, I see you!
You are loved.
Just be YOU,
And nothing more."

She came face to face
With her
PROSTITUTE
Who didn't want to admit
The ways she had sold herself -

Sacrificing her beliefs
In exchange
For more wealth.

And then she came
Face to face
With her own
SABOTEUR
The voice that kept
Her safe,
But left out.

Always finding ways
To get stuck
By justifying
Her doubts.

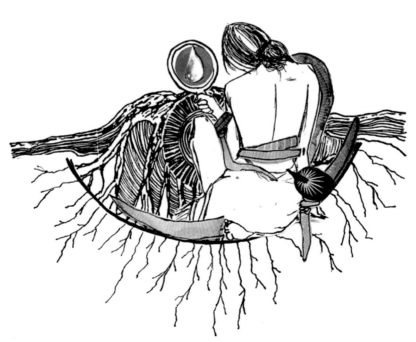

"I think I found the poison,"
Said the STUMP.

"I knew you would,"
Whispered the MOON.

"It's been here all along,"
Said the STUMP.

"You found the medicine,"
Whispered the MOON.

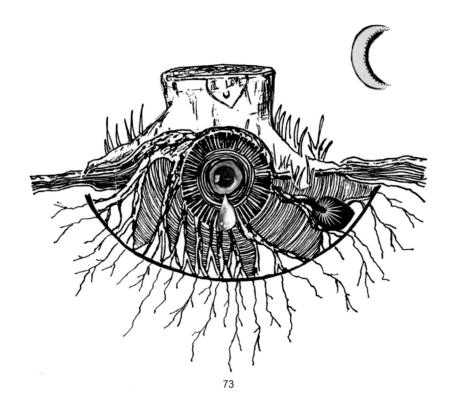

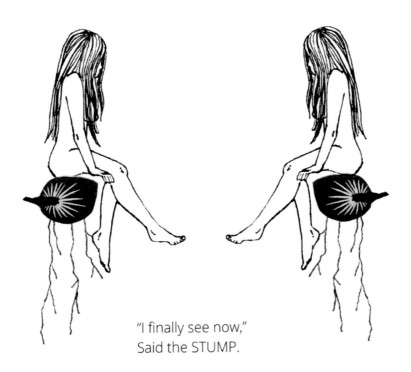

"I finally see now,"
Said the STUMP.

"We're all MIRRORS
To each other,
Reflecting our Fears
Where we must jump.

And I digest poison
By coming face to face
With my own ROOTS."

"That is part of it,"
Whispered the MOON,
"But you must also find the
FRUIT."

"But I will have to start over!"
Complained the STUMP.

"It will take me years
Before I grow fruit!"

"That is true,"
Whispered the MOON,

"But you hold
MAGIC in your ROOTS."

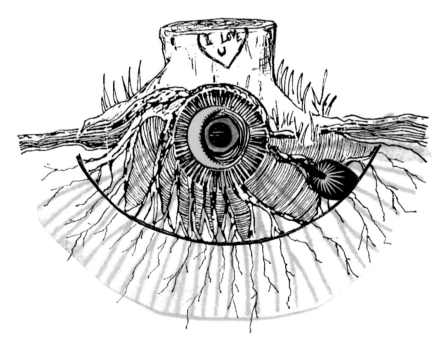

"What is MAGIC?"
Asked the STUMP.

"It is
The Great
I AM -
Spirit Divine.

She offers
Mystic Power and Wisdom
From our ancient Bloodline."

"How do I find this MAGIC?"
Asked the STUMP.

"By expanding outward,"
Whispered the STARS.

"Now that you've
Rooted down
To find the medicine,
It is time to share this
With others,"
Whispered the STARS.

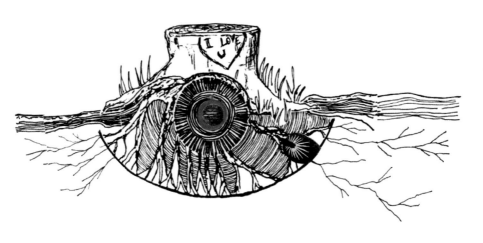

"But how will I find them?"
Asked the STUMP,
"If I have to expand
In the dark,
Underground?"

"You will find them
By feeling
In your HEART,
The Unstruck Sound."

"So I have to
Trust myself,"
The STUMP sighed.

"You can do it,"
Whispered the STARS.
"Just listen to your Guide."

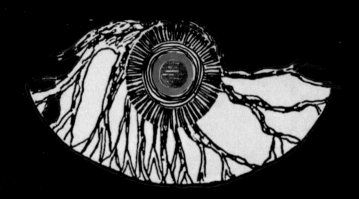

And so the STUMP
Began her journey,
Feeling her way through
The Unseen.

Trusting her intuition,
Guidance suddenly appeared
From a Queen.

Her name alone
Holds ancient power.
From MAIDEN
To MOTHER
Then wise CRONE.

A Red Thread weaves
The story
Of an unexpected
Miracle grown.

Some know her as
The Virgin,
But she is also the
Prostitute.

She came as a
Poet, Artist, and Musician -
Singing us her
FRUIT.

"Listen in,
Sweet child.
I offer nourishment
For you to drink.

This nectar
comes from a
ROSE
Grown from the
Thoughts you think.

WHAT YOU BELIEVE
IS WHAT YOU BECOME.

Tears and nectar
Hold an Elixir.

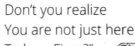

Don't you realize
You are not just here
To be a Fixer?"

So the STUMP
Sipped the nectar
And closed her
Eyes.

Her own tears swelled
When she acknowledged
Her own
Lies.

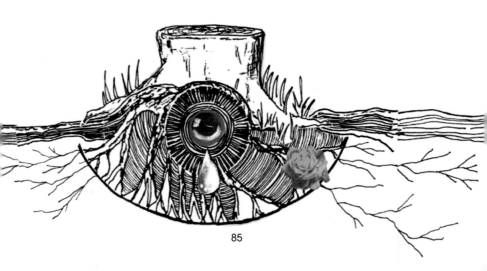

"I've always looked
For something
Or someone else
To blame.

But now I see
That we are all
Very much
The same."

"The path to healing
Is Forgiveness
And surrender
To the unknown...

But Forgiveness
Of **THE SELF**
Is the KEY to
FREEDOM!"
Spoke the CRONE.

And with that,
Every Tear was named.

All the others.
All her own -
With nothing left to be blamed.

A cracking
Open.
Light poured in from
Above.

Her Tears
Became the
Rain.
She blossomed
In her own
LOVE.

From every ROOT
Grew a garden,
Full of vibrant
Nourishment
Of plenty.

All the others
Returned to help
Weed and harvest
For many.

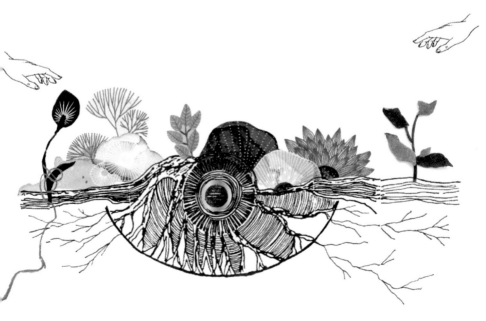

And then with
Great surrender,
The ROOTS
Took a deep breath
And exhaled their last.

It was now time
For the WIND
To carry her away
From the past.

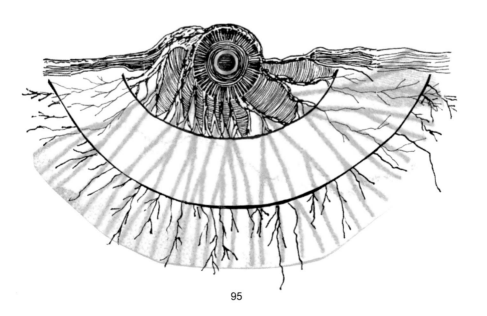

"Where am I going now?"
Asked the ROOTS.

"You'll see."
Smiled the EARTH.

"You're healing is complete,"
Sprinkled the rains of WATER,
"Now you know your own worth."

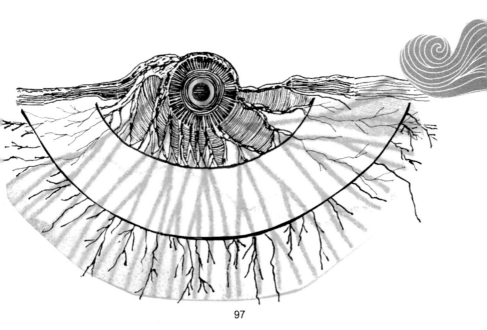

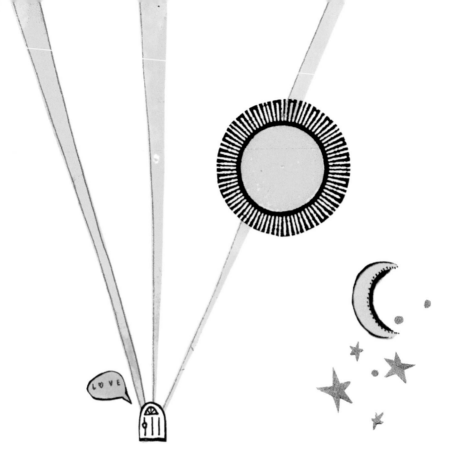

"You followed your Heart,"
Burned the FIRE.

"You learned to digest poison,"
Beamed the SUN.

"You found forgiveness,"
Cried the MOON.

"And you let yourself shine!"
Shouted the STARS,
"You didn't run!"

The ROOTS began
To soften.
They released -
Then let go.

Closing her eyes
She whispered,
"Now I know."

And with that,
She spread her wings
All on her own.

"You now FLY FREE.
It's time for your rebirth,"
Sang the CRONE.

THE END.

The magic behind all creations is the personal story of the creator. Kim Krans writes in *The Wild Unknown Archetypes Guidebook* that THE CREATOR is "The Artist, The Alchemist, The Innovator." When we witness others courageously offer their creative gifts to the world: be it words, poetry, art, music, dance, or whatever, a SEED is planted. Perhaps it takes root in many, or just in one individual. That message, intention, or piece of beauty is then alchemized into a creation of its own. It is in this ripple effect of sharing our creative expressions that we get to participate in the true healing power of Art as a collective.

Just before the poetic journey of THE SEED began on the Scorpio Full Moon (April 26, 2021), in the pages of my journal (#37), I wrote these words:

This is true: I fear my own Light.
My brilliant power and knowing of what I have
To be SEEN...
And at the same time, I grieve that the world may not see what I see.

I know this may sound absurd, but during the beginning of 2021, I grew a cutaneous horn (purple in color) from the very top of my forehead, and I called it my "Unicorn Horn." I also grew a wart at the end of my tailbone, or "Root Chakra." When I had it removed, the black scar left on my head looked exactly like the circular Spirit symbol drawn on the top of the Unicorn card from Kim Kran's *The Wild Unknown Animal Spirit* deck. The Unicorn symbol means: *Reconnecting to Higher Wisdom or Divinity.*

This *"root"* wart and black *"seed"* remained on my head and tailbone until the poetic words of THE SEED were finally written.

THE UNICORN
AND THE SIXTH CHAKRA

It's no surprise the subtle essence of the Unicorn card resides at the third eye, the exact place from which the Unicorn's horn extends. This center is called the Ajna chakra, or "command center." The ancient yogis believed it to be responsible for our intellect, intuition, snd deepest wisdom. Some say our two eyes see the past and present, while this third eye peers into the future.

- Kim Krans

The Wild Unknown
Animal Spirit Guidebook (p. 203)

On the night before completing The SEED's final illustration, I had a dream...

OCT. 31st, 2021
Everything was in black and white. I was walking along a wild grown pathway that opened between two orchards. A strong Storm was brewing, like what Dorthy experienced in the Wizard of Oz, just before the Twister hit. White paper diamonds were flying all around me sideways, and the path became unclear before me. I stood still, as silence suddenly caused everything to stop in place.

The paper white diamonds turned to Unicorns surrounding me. There were hundreds of them, but still in black and white. I was then taken to a waiting place to determine my lineage connected to them. As I awoke, I remembered these wise words:

"You've always had the power my dear. You just had to learn it for yourself."
-Glinda (The Wizard Of Oz)

There are too many "Red Threads" to count all the ways I have experienced my healing journey. The SEED led me to the deeper exploration of family secrets, betrayal, my sexuality and queerness. I am still following that "Red Thread" as I integrate all these parts of myself on the journey through forgiveness and freedom to SHINE my authentic self.

That story of JADE MAGIC is still unfolding and being told.

May we all see our own story within The SEED of the Self each time it is read. May the magic reveal your own mirrors of TRUTH as you examine your own Roots.

Photographer: Julianna Clausen Maul, 2021
@BlushArtistriesPhotography

JADE's birth name is Erin Joy Cummings. After a series of prophetic dreams and a near death experience, she now calls herself JADE, or JADE MAGIC, meaning "Ancient Wisdom, Healer of Hearts." Jade identifies as a magical queer woman who is also an artist, poet, astrologer, dancer, mystic, & dreamer... a true Pisces Mermaid! Her background began with a BA in Fine Arts at Oregon State University with an emphasis in Print Making & Design. Later she became a Fitness Instructor, Personal Trainer, and Nutritional Therapy Practitioner. This experience led her to start her own private practice in 2013 for holistic health, focusing on Transformational Counseling & Wellness. The Covid-19 Pandemic brought her back to her love and hunger of creating Art and Poetry. JADE and her Soulmate, Rick, live in Southern Oregon. Together, they returned back to their roots in 2018, along with their chocolate labradoodle, Luna Rose.

THE CREATIONS

I specifically wanted to weave together the illustrations of THE SEED by bringing in my own pen & ink drawings with paper collage from other inspiring artists' creations. The SEED illustration itself is cut from the spirit symbol of the Unicorn card in *The Wild Unknown Animal Spirit Deck* by Kim Krans. As the SEED moves through its life cycles in my illustrations, it intentionally changes colors to represent the 7 Chakras. I found many of my collage pieces from *ORIGIN.MAGAZINE* (Volume 44) by Miranda Pleasant. I was inspired by Caroline Myss, in her book, *Sacred Contracts*, revealing the Archetypes of the Victim, Child, Prostitute, and Saboteur. I felt drawn to a unique process in which all the parts of my illustrations remained loose and mobile, photographed and pieced together to create a nonpermanent state, just like Life itself.

I feel it is important to mention several more empowered POETS, ARTISTS & MUSICIANS who have inspired my journey thus far. I offer my gratitude for the SEEDS they have planted.

Thank you to the late poets, Mary Oliver & Rumi, and the very much alive, Rupi Kaur. Thank you to the *untamed love warrior*, Glennon Doyle, and the *vulnerable & daring* Brené Brown, Ph.D. Thank you to Elizabeth Gilbert for inspiring me to journey through my own *EAT, PRAY, LOVE* adventure to discovering my *Big Magic*. Thank you Clarissa Pinkola Estés, Ph.D. for reminding me of my Wild Woman Archetype. Thank you to my Astrology teachers, Debra Silverman and Chani Nicholas, for bringing me the language of The Stars and deeper insights of my own beautiful Natal Chart. Deepest gratitudes to the healing music of Trevor Hall and Brandi Carlile, who were with me in the darkest and sweetest hours. And a special gratitude to my Soul Brother, Jeremiah Zuba, for not only his sacred gifts of meditation guidance and the "Virgo Eye" of refinement, but his courageous queerness and playfulness that has nourished my Inner Child.

To all my FAMILY, thank you for your support and continual love as you have witnessed me in constant transformation. This is the story of ME, but it is also the story of US.

To Rick, my Life Partner, Best Friend, Soulmate, and Lover...

Thank you for *loving me and seeing me.* More importantly, thank you for loving & seeing *yourself.* Thank you for continuing to grow and transform through the MIRRORS we are to one another. I am grateful for our Sacred Union over many lifetimes.

Made in the USA
Las Vegas, NV
23 March 2022

46154250R00074